EXCERPTS
FROM THE DIARIES OF
THE LATE GOD

EXCERPTS
FROM THE DIARIES OF
THE LATE GOD

Selected and Edited by ANTHONY TOWNE

with illustrations by Barton Lidicé Beneš

HARPER & ROW, PUBLISHERS

NEW YORK, EVANSTON, AND LONDON

Acknowledgment: "God is Dead in Georgia," copyrighted © 1966 by The
Board of Education of The Methodist Church, is used by permission of
motive magazine.

FIRST EDITION

LIBRARY OF CONGRESS CATALOG CARD NUMBER: 68–11740

FOR

WILLIAM STRINGFELLOW and RAY KARRAS
for whom God exists; for whom God exists not;

FROM

ANTHONY TOWNE
who, faithful, he trusts, to Christ,
wholly agrees with both of them.

And when Moses went into the tent of the meeting to speak with the Lord, he heard the voice speaking to him from above the mercy seat that was upon the ark of the testimony, from between the two cherubim; and it spoke to him.

—*Numbers* 7:89 (RSV)

God's self-communication *to* us has a certain consequence *in* us, namely, that when he communicates himself to us God then truly "lives" in us.

—Leslie Dewart, *The Future of Belief,*
Herder and Herder, 1966, p. 142.

EXCERPTS
FROM THE DIARIES OF
THE LATE GOD

Prefatory Caveats

After the unfortunate death of the late God in the autumn of 1965, it was generally accepted that the process of divine revelation had also come to its end. Dead gods, some declared, tell no tales. This hasty conclusion has proved to be without foundation. The deeply lamented Supreme Being, it turns out, characteristically fore-sighted, had scrupulously kept, throughout his protracted reign, meticulous diaries of the events attendant upon it. The personal effects and properties of the departed deity were not, of course, available for human inspection, and his diaries might well have been consigned—so far as we are concerned—to an everlasting limbo, had they not, in circumstances quite remarkable, been discovered by (more precisely, *disclosed to*) a humble layman and carpenter of words, canonically resident, at that time, in the Episcopal Diocese of New York, namely: me.

It would be the height of presumption on my part to speculate as to why I, of all miserable sinners, should have been chosen as the *vehicle* for these, the very last of ultimate revelations. The fact, as it were, speaks for itself. Certainly no one ought, on account of this unique burden, impute to me any merit beyond the ordinary, if that. More pertinent, surely, is the sad happenstance that it fell to me to compose, for *The New York Times* and *motive* magazine, the obituary of God, a document included at the end of this book for the benefit of readers who superstitiously skip that fascinating page of the estimable *Times,* and which contains a full report of the cir-cumstances surrounding that most grievous of deaths and the reac-tion of the world to it. I can only suppose that my obituary, inade-quate though it humanly had to be, somewhat pleased the powers that be—or should I say: *the powers that remain?* I suggest, in other words, that the incumbent authorities hoped from me in editing and selecting from God's diaries the same objectivity and good taste I strove to impart to the obituary. To that modest standard I have, in any event, pledged myself.

Now, a few words as to the *nature* of the diaries may be in order.

I am frequently asked what language God chose for his most intimate confidings. The fact of the matter is he employed *all* languages (as it were *simultaneously*), including a great many unknown to me and which I presume to be languages of other planets, possibly even planets of other solar systems. There are a few languages that *may* be languages that will appear on earth in the future, a speculation I entertain because of some resemblances to extant tongues, notably Chinese and Tagalog. I have confined myself, however, to the text as rendered in English, mainly because it is the language in which I feel most at home. I *have* examined some entries in other languages, and can recommend the French for elegance while warning against the German, which is ponderous. No text, oddly, appears in Latin, an exception I explain, tentatively, as a reflection of God's passionate antipathy, while he was alive, toward all forms of death, including dead languages.

Internal evidence persuades me that God *thought* in Aramaic.

There has been, my publishers tell me, widespread interest in what might be called the physical characteristics of the diaries. Scarcely a day passes that I am not stopped on the street by a wag with a skeptical smirk on his face, and asked: "Did God use a fountain pen?" (More inventive wags substitute: "quill pen," "typewriter," "invisible ink," "skywriting," and so forth.) Sophisticates commonly hazard that given the multilingual nature of the diaries some sort of computer must have been used. Here again, the answer has to be that God employed all these devices and many others, including, for example, carving on stone tablets. I have relied almost entirely upon the typewritten version because I find God's penmanship indecipherable, and computers are foreign to my comprehension. God's stone carving, on the other hand, is stunning, but handling so heavy a volume of tablets is too burdensome. Listen-

ing to the taped versions is certainly entertaining, but unfortunately my attention tends to wander. God favored dramatic pauses.

Many requests come my way to produce the diaries physically, either to authenticate that they exist or to satisfy a natural curiosity about them. The Keeper of Rare Books at Yale, as an example, offered to *empty* the Sterling Memorial Library if I would consent to an exhibition of the diaries. Now I would be *delighted* to make the diaries available under *any* suitable auspices if I could. But I cannot. The fact of the matter is the diaries were not *physically* produced to *me*. They did not, after all, just fall out of a tree one day when I happened to pass beneath, and if they *had* I daresay I would still be digging myself out from under.

No, the diaries, in fact, presented themselves to me *as objects of my imagination*. The key word there is: *objects*. I must stress that the diaries most definitely are *not* subjective projections out of my own banal fantasies. It happened—the discovery (or disclosure) of the diaries—this way: One day in the late spring of 1966, Whitsunday, as it chanced to be, a violent downpour having washed out my customary postprandial stroll, I undertook, in its place, a leisurely excursion through my dry and somnolent imagination, where I came upon, to my utter astonishment, certain *objects* which proved, upon examination, to be the diaries of the late God. It was as simple and unextraordinary as that! Given the nature of the diaries *and* their exceptional source, was it not inevitable and even *natural* (surely not *super*natural) that they should have arrived into this fallen estate exactly that way? So it seemed, and seems, to me, no matter what interpretation others may *seek* to foist upon it.

My greatest problem as editor of the diaries has been, of course, that of *selection* from the literally endless proliferation of entries those which it seemed to me would most edify present-day folk. I have had to be *ruthlessly* arbitrary. Whole categories of entries of enchanting interest I have had to toss out broadside. Throughout I have endeavored to be pertinaciously objective. Entries of little interest to me have been included out of deference to those many readers with tastes more capacious than my own. I have, on that ground alone, kept in a number of entries reflecting

4

the deceased deity's bemusement with human sex, although I have taken care to exclude any such entries plainly violative of commonly accepted moral standards. God, it is my solemn duty to report, perhaps because he was a bachelor, was somewhat vulnerable to prurient literature.

In fairness to readers of the diaries it may be useful if I define, as best I can, the criteria which have governed my selection of those entries which survive in this brief digest:

(1) An overwhelming majority of entries have to do with other planets and solar systems—upwards of 99 per cent, as a matter of fact—and all of these I have eliminated since they obviously have no immediate bearing upon *our* affairs.

(2) An alarmingly small number of entries have to do with future events on *this* planet, and I have reluctantly excluded all of them on the argument that God would not have intended that we foreknow the future, especially since if we did we might attempt to change it, which could result in all sorts of confusion that would be a disservice to his memory.

(3) A surprising volume of entries has to do with events or personages of which or of whom there is, so far as I am aware, no historical record; and again I have excluded most of these because they would be of interest only to a handful of pedants.

(4) There are, I must candidly say, not a few entries which are unquestionably scandalous, including some that pertain to living persons (*L*yndon *B*aines *J*ohnson, for example, whom God sometime calls "the monogram madcap") and border on libel; other entries, while not strictly libelous, fall outside the bounds of good taste; certain entries would, I fear, be deemed heretical in some circles. All such entries, for obvious reasons, have been resolutely purged.

(5) I have found that innumerable entries depart substantially from historical fact. Here I have allowed what leeway I responsibly could to God's judgment, which is manifestly more reliable than my own; but not even God, after all, can fly in the face of facts. All of the entries I have included will be found to conform—in every important respect—with history as we know it to be. God, I feel sure, would have wanted it that way.

(6) God, as might be supposed, devoted much of his diaries to other deities, and I have included some of this, but where, as is often the case, he speaks condescendingly of his near peers, I have thought it only prudent to make excisions, particularly in instances of deities of living religions; ecumenism, one of the late God's favorite charities, would scarcely benefit from an untimely disclosure of what can only be called transcendental gossip.

A word needs to be said about the *numeration* of the diaries, which might otherwise puzzle some readers. God, as everyone knows, did not dwell in time but in eternity—a horse, if I may mix my metaphor, of a different color—and the entries in his diaries are not, therefore, chronological. His numeration is, nonetheless, *sequential*. Now, I myself was puzzled, for a time, as to the nature of that sequence, assuming, stupidly, that the entries had been numbered *in the order in which they were written*. Not so; it turns out, as any good Christian would expect, that God numbered the entries *in the order in which they are to be read!* (The mind of God is—or *was*—simplicity itself.) In this sadly slender, harshly truncated selection, of course, readers will find the numeration, while remaining sequential, drastically erratic, countless entries having been, as explained, excluded. The numbers, by the way, are Roman rather than Arabic, an eccentricity I attribute to God's disdain for the religion of Islam, a competitive enterprise. A book could be written—and no doubt several will—about the late God's penchant for petulance.

It will dismay many of God's more enlightened adherents, but I am obliged to record that the deity was a firm believer in astrology. The evidence in the diaries permits no other surmise. Readers will note that entries in the diaries are dated according to zodiacal signs. Each sign of the zodiac, according to my exegesis, represents an *age*. Within each such sign or age some thirty *aeons* are contained. *Thus*, there *might* be an entry dated: "CAPRICORN+ XIV." That would mean, as I get it, that the entry reflects upon an event which took place in the *fourteenth aeon of capricornage*. (Actually there is *no* such entry in the diaries, and I use it randomly as an example only. Nothing worth mentioning, I presume, *happened* in the fourteenth aeon of capricornage.) Much more could be said about the way eternity is divided, but the whole subject is fraught with imponderables, and anyhow, it would take us much too far afield. A solid editor, I hold, keeps two feet firmly planted in the particular field he is tilling.

This is not the place, nor have I the competence, to undertake an exegesis of the diaries, nor would such an exegesis merit serious study if it were based solely upon this impoverished selection without reference to the entire *corpus* of the diaries. Still, it might be of limited usefulness were I to outline certain themes that seem to me to emerge from the entries I have selected. Readers might otherwise feel that they have been peremptorily hurled into multitudinous seas, uncharted. In general: *God clearly found it almost as difficult to comprehend the human condition as we humans find it to comprehend the divine condition.* That is the essential purport of this, his terminal revelation. Specifically, then, and merely as I see it, the diaries engage the following issues:

    (a) *God's perplexity about time*
    (b) *God's perplexity about death*
    (c) *God's perplexity about women*
    (d) *God's perplexity about prayer*
    (e) *God's perplexity about money*
    (f) *God's perplexity about church*
    (g) *God's perplexity about theology*
    (h) *God's perplexity about morals*

Now these are all themes, needless to say, that have preoccupied humankind from time immemorial, and this ought not to surprise us; *but* allow me to point out that God's perplexity differs radically from our own and does so *markedly*. Therein, I submit, rests the peculiar immediacy the diaries have *for us*. God, through his unique diaries, struggling to see things *under the aspect of time* has enormously, and as it were *gratuitously*, assisted us in our struggle to see things *under the aspect of eternity*.

Readers will be cheered or outraged to discover that I have eschewed the paraphernalia of scholarship in assembling this onerous compilation. There is no index. There are no footnotes. There is no appendix. God's diaries, in my considered opinion, sparkle with a clarity so luminous as to banish all the instruments mankind has devised to reticulate obfuscation. Is there a reader with soul so dense who does not know that J.C. is Jesus Christ, God's son? Is there a reader with soul so depraved who does not know that the H.G. is the Holy Ghost, confidante of the deity, mentor of the son? Such a reader, if such there be, might prefer to repair to the Holy Bible, which will answer more questions for him than ever in a lifetime he can hope to ask. An attitude of acceptance is more cleanly than godliness. As God himself says somewhere in the diaries, it is more blessed to receive than to give, and more difficult.

It has not been difficult, I must concede, for me to receive from Barton Lidicé Beneš the *inspired* illustrations that lighten the pages of this volume. He has given to the work that remarkable talent which made him a favorite artist of the late God, whose private study included several original and impudent Beneš' creations. God once said that his creation was best served by those who had the sense to imitate it. Barton Beneš has had the wit to do precisely that. That is why God specified that he should illustrate the diaries.

Further from my mind than the royalties could not be my desperate anxiety to acknowledge the assistance I have received in preparing God's diaries for publication. My cup runs over. I could not have selected from the diaries had God not written them. Edward Ziegler, himself an editor, having heard that the diaries had fallen into my possession, stressed to me my obligation to share them with the world. Deeply I bow to yet another editor for yet another publisher, nameless here, Mr. Arthur Buckley, whose patient indulgence of idiosyncrasy (on my part) eloquently testifies that God, upon his death, did not *bury* all his wisdom in the *Sea*. Several verities, in fact, have survived God's demise, among them friendship, which allows me the joy of a salute to Dr. and Mrs. Robert Klopstock. It was from Ray Karras that I first learned I had been commissioned to write God's obituary, and from that melancholy assignment much has followed; in the unlikely event that I predecease him, I would be honored should Mr. Karras be profligate enough to write *my* obituary. I affirm of William String-fellow that were it not for his witness my relations with the late

God would by now have deteriorated to such a point that his diaries could not have been entrusted to my meager custody. No one has helped me in any way with the arduous chore of typing the manuscript.

ANTHONY TOWNE

Many Sundays after Trinity, 1967

I am bored with it all.

Here I sit. I am omniscient. I am omnipotent. I am omnipresent. I am divine. I am supreme. I am ineffable. I am, in short, God. But I am condemned to look out interminably in all directions into an impenetrable void.

Small wonder that wretched, horny-tailed ingrate walked out on me.

If only I had *something* to do! Something *creative!*

I am omnibored.

Sitting in the garden this morning, after tea, staring into the deep as I have done more mornings than I could count on the flicks of my eye, suddenly there came to me, as though out of nothing—*ex nihilo?*—a thought so simple and yet so profound I fancied I had experienced an emotion.

I am that I am.

Could ultimate truth be reduced to a more gritty kernel? What troubles me, however, is the utter simplicity of the thought, which has to be accounted either metaphysical or merely redundant. What does it mean? I do not know, but somehow I can't escape a feeling of anticipation. Candor compels me to confess it: finally, after all these futile eternities, finally and suddenly, perhaps because I have chosen a new blend of tea, I seem to be on to something really big!

I am so full of myself I think I could create a world.

I have created the heavens and the earth!

Alpha to omega, what a week it has been! It all came off without any unfixable hitch, exactly as I had worked it out in my scale model. I *did* discover when I had finished up Adam that I had a rib in there that was completely superfluous. I hate waste, so I took the thing out and made a woman out of it. That does worry me some because she wasn't part of the original plan and I'm not clear just how she'll fit in, if I may put it that way. Perhaps the H.G. was right that I should have tossed the rib in the soup kettle along with the leftover greens. But if everything had turned out precisely according to plan there would have been no room for the unexpected. *That's* been the trouble up here. Nothing *ever* goes wrong!

The toughest part of it was setting it all up so that later on their geologists and paleontologists and whatnots will be able to satisfy themselves that it all happened naturally and in no way violated the evolutionary process. I carefully included skeletons of pre-historic monsters, remnants of a missing link, bits of meteorites from other planets, rock formations that might have been caused by glacial erosion, and so on. I wanted there to be sufficient evidence to rule out absolutely any suggestion that my creation was some sort of *supernatural* phenomenon. There was nothing whatever supernatural about it! It was blood, sweat, and tears, if you want to know the truth. There is nothing the least bit spooky, believe me, about plain hard work.

What a satisfaction to have had a dream, to have nurtured and tended it, and finally to have seen it *become* reality! Not to mention the relief that no longer must I look out from the breakfast nook on that neck of the yeasty deep that just sat there useless and reproachful. How many times the H.G. inflicted upon me his wretched pun: "Excellency, when are you going to do something with that *abysmal* eyesore?" Ha! Ha! Well, I *have* done something with it, and I have seen that it is good. Seldom do I indulge in self-congratulations, but on this, the first of my very own Sunday mornings, I make a warranted exception.

Man, I well foreknew, was pushing a good thing *too* far. Why could I not have been content with the birds and the beasts and the fishes? And the cattle, bless them, chewing away *uncomplaining* on their redundant cuds? I should have stopped at the least with creeping things. Serpents I had to include as a sop to His Horny-tailed Nibs; even the devil has to have some sort of bottom to slip into, else what are bottoms for? But a creature capable of imagining he possesses *intelligence?* That is transparently risky and a folly. From imagined intelligence will surely be concocted the sin that dares not speak its name: *free will.* It will be no use my quoting to them Dante: "In His will is our peace." (*In sua volonte e nostra pace.*) They won't believe a word of it. I have made, in J.C.'s words, a colossal blunder, and poor J.C. may have to pay for it. The sins of the fathers are visited upon the sons. Why, oh why, did I yield to that accursed lagniappe?

I wanted someone to share it with. Famous last words. Well, I had better get on with plans for J.C.'s incarnation. Four thousand years are about how long I figure I can put it off. And allowing for that element of the unexpected I frivolously introduced, I had better set it for 4004 years. God's work is never done.

I am the only deity—so far as I know (and after all I *am* omniscient)—to have a whale for a pet.

Esther is mischievous but lovable. She gets into more trouble than a cloudful of harp-players. She eats me out of house and mansions. She *will* not stay out of the H.G.'s dovecote. But I wouldn't part with her for the Judgment Seat. She has a coy twinkle in her eye that would melt old Ahab's flinty heart. And she is loyal to a fault. Let the H.G. flounce into my office to complain that I refuse to make up my mind about some trivial earth-war and swift as Mercury old Esther will drench his tacky burnoose with a spoutful of ambrosia. When the old goat turns to see from whence came this sweet offense, Esther will greet him with a beatific countenance that seems to say: "Who, me?" More fun than turning Lot's wife into a pillar of salt.

But I stray from my story. What has Miss Esther done now but swallow that caterwauling creep from Nineveh. Doom, doom, and more doom is all the wretched man can think of. Well, old Esther gave him a taste of his own doom. Swallowed him whole and kept him three days in her blubbery belly. He was like to die. Tears rolled down my cheeks and my voice was so choked with belly

laughs it was three days before I could bellow: "Spit him out, for the love of Baal, before you get a tummy-ache." And spit crazy Jonah out she did, leaving him sprawled helpless on the beach. It was the first time he had been sober since he discovered there was intoxication in prophecy. I was so entertained I decided to spare Nineveh, and also much cattle. And I gave old Esther that pillar of salt so the pool would be more to her taste.

If I didn't know I am perfect I would suspect I've been possessed by a demon.

It's this business of my "sake." What in limbo do they mean when they speak of God's sake? Over and over again I hear them: *"For God's sake!"* What sake? I have no sake. Yet they invoke it so often I sometimes think they revere my sake more than me myself. I have had my entire estate inventoried item by item and have found no sake and nothing even resembling one.

Could they mean that toenail of Pregod I wear round my neck as talisman of the pregone bliss? How could they? I have never told them about that. Ah, Pregod, of blessed memory, about whom I remember precisely nothing; Author, indeed, precisely of that nothing out of which it was my destiny to create something; Cause, indeed, of that causelessness out of which emerged First Cause, Me; Vocabulator, indeed, of that primeval speechlessness which gave utterance to Alpha *and* Omega; Very Pregod of Very Pregod; Predark of Predark; Prebegotten of the unbegotten; Who precedeth from nothingness, nada and nullity; Who is of one Preinsubsantiality with Presubstantiality; Whose Kingdom shall have no beginning and whose end is endless. Ah, Theology, Queen of Heaven, marvelous are thy works and splendid thy rhetoric!

But I forget myself, so to speak. About that infernal sake. As I say, I have searched high and low, every mansion, but not a trace of a sake. J.C. suggested it might be a physical complaint or some sort or an organ I didn't know I had. So, off I went to the doctor for an exhaustive battery of tests, which turned up nothing more interesting than a slightly inflamed spleen and a tender *omnipotens*.

There *is,* the H.G. reports, a Japanese liquor called *sake*— pronounced, however, as in tACKY. But everybody knows I never touch any hard liquor. J.C. is supposed to have a sake, too, and Isis only knows *what* he drinks, but with his hang-up on poverty I doubt he could afford anything.

I give up. For the sake of my peace of mind I shall brood on the matter no more.

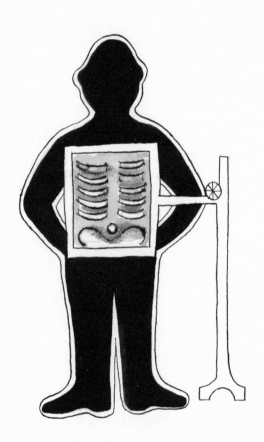

Billy Graham has halitosis of the soul.

I set down here without further comment an exchange of memoranda between the H.G. and myself:

From the Desk of the H.G.

G: Your attention is once again directed to the *scandal* of sex among earthfolk. In bedrooms and back seats, igloos and palaces, public parks and choir lofts—*everywhere*—the shameless creatures are perpetrating unspeakable intimacies. One would think sex had something to do with pleasure. Mindful of your request for specific data I have undertaken, reluctantly, exhaustive research. I am *not* a pornographer! You will receive from me no titillations, no impurities, no material calculated solely to incite prurient interest. My method has been clinical; my objective is action; my zeal is compassion; my anguish is immense. What I have been compelled in line of duty to witness would nauseate Dr. Freud. I append to this report (*For Your Eyes Only*) photographs to document the prevalence down there of the following atrocious immoralities: kissing, petting, fondling, groping, caressing, making love. I can't go on! I am beside myself! See for yourself. It is utterly disgusting. Such conditions simply cannot be tolerated. I pray that the Front Office will take prompt, effective, and punitive action. Something must be done.

Directive from the Front Office

H.G.: I have reviewed with care the unnecessarily voluminous documentation you have submitted to substantiate your charge that there is sex on earth. I am persuaded. I have found the material frequently amusing, sometimes repulsive, often banal and wholly irrelevant. It is no concern of mine how earthfolk entertain themselves. You have established that they amuse themselves in remarkably maladroit ways. That is their problem. Given the mischief they are prone to get into, sex seems to me the least of it. Might I have at long last your report on the question of money?

Blast that Myrtle! She's supposed to be my secretary, not my nursemaid. Every month when a new *Playboy* comes up from down there the dratted woman removes the centerfold before hurling what's left into my IN box. I, to whom all hearts are open, all desires known, and from whom no secrets are hid, am denied, by a meddlesome frump, erotic titillations available to any prep-school freshman. But I fixed her wagon. Plump in the middle of this morning's routine taped dictation I slipped a delicious limerick, a most amusing trifle—picked up from John XXIII—about the Bishop of Birmingham and a boy from Bulgaria.

Finally, I took in a performance of Mr. Albee's *Tiny Alice*.

Theater is not my cup of tea, though I adore movies/ But I have to confess that Albee is a sly one. His play is blasphemy. I should punish him severely—which I suspect he'd enjoy—but he has a way of making *me* enjoy *his* arrant impudence.

I rather think he's in love with me.

What can I say? Tiny Alice is a ventriloquist, and Edward Albee is her dummy.

Parlor games amuse him. When he wends his wayward way up here I have several parlor games I'm saving just for him.

Take care, Edward, my son.

No, Margaret Truman, I do *not* have a white beard!

I am not fastidious about my person, but I *am* slightly private about it. I do not believe in flaunting myself, reasonably intact and comely though I am. But something *must* be said. I will not go down in eternity encumbered with the legends they have invented about what I look like. Leave it to them and I'll have the gills of a blowfish, the hooves of a hyena, the wings of a hoot owl, and the torso of a platypus. Look what they have done to some of the most decent deities ever to have graced the shabby gentility of pantheon!

I *do* have a beard, of course, which I shave, save for my rakish goatee, a vanity I allow myself because I've been told the carrot color enhances my olive complexion. My eyes—two only—are ovaltine set off against white tending toward a reddish yellow. I have, Myrtle says, a prominent nose, sculptural ears, a firm jaw, and full lips. Having fluoridated the deep I am thankful to report that I have a complete set of *natural* teeth. I am virtually bald, as befits my intellectual proclivities. I trust I will not be accounted immodest when I aver that I have all the customary organs and parts *and* as of last check all are in good working condition.

My height is problematical but in earth measure I would judge it to be generously upwards of six feet. My weight is a sore point with me. Reduced to avoirdupois I gauge it at two hundred pounds and then some, more than it should be, no doubt, but what can I do? Beyond a few desultory push-ups and a daily swim I am disinclined toward exercise. Diets are commendable when coupled with fasting, but having nothing for which to fast I cannot see what I would gain by giving up eating.

In *my* job there are precious few consolations, and what there are I husband with consummate resourcefulness. Nothing ventured, J.C. likes to say, nothing lost! Play against the odds and the odds are you'll come out ahead. I should know.

My medical history is impeccable. I surrendered my tonsils early on. From the outset there has been a certain tenderness in my *omnipotens.* Now and then my hypostasis slips out of kilter. Other than that I am in superb condition. The H.G. insists I live what he calls a dissolute existence. But he's the one with the nervous stomach and the hypertension. Whatever it is I do, I must be doing something right!

A word only about my attire. I wear pants! I have never worn a skirt. Whenever possible I wear shorts. Underwear has always struck me as confining. Sandals are excellent footgear, but bare feet are more suitable for most situations. I use no scents except occasionally a touch of something Esther makes up every Easter. Jewelry is personally obnoxious to me. For general audiences, however, I do wear a plain wooden cross J.C. gave me when he got back from his catastrophic undertaking below. It is, strange to say, the sole *memento mori* I own.

I cannot resist ample Harry Truman style patterned sport shirts.

I want to settle, for the record, the problem of the chicken and the egg.

The chicken came first, later a rooster, and shortly thereafter the egg.

The situation is reversed, however, in the case of turtles. First off was the egg, or rather many eggs, somewhat later many turtles, shortly many more eggs and so on.

If I possessed any authority on earth—and Mammon knows I don't—I would insist that every church building carry on its facade a blinking neon sign:

GOD IS HUMAN, TOO!

I thought I made that abundantly clear in the Incarnation, but the point doesn't seem to have gotten across. (Puns are the sneakiest rascals.) The fact that I'm perfect doesn't exempt me from headaches; on the contrary, it only insures that my headaches are perfect—perfectly awful, in fact. I grasp what Fiorello La-Guardia meant when he said: "When I make a mistake, it's a beaut!" In my case, Little Flower, a mistake's a disaster.

Take color. Rainbows worked out fine. I experimented first with solid bands of a single primary color and the effects were striking but somehow, I thought, too heavy. So, I substituted ribbons of several colors, and set against the blue of the sky, nothing lovelier occurs anywhere in creation. Really very simple to make and inexpensive—just water and light—but utterly satisfying. If only I'd had the sense to stick to simple things I do well and to stay away from complicated things that strain my gifts and really—I must face it—don't come off.

Anyway, happy about rainbows, when I was working through the preliminary sketches for man I had what I thought was the inspired idea to make him in different colors. Disaster isn't the half of it! The basic mistake—my hindsight has always been more acute than my foresight—was to deviate from primary colors. White, so enchanting in the empyrean, comes over as *colorlessness* in the creation. *Blah* is the word for it. While I did what I could to rectify the error by making J.C. a jet black, the *blah* people, understandably I guess, refuse to admit that I could have made a mistake.

I make a mistake. I humiliate myself by admitting it. I carefully point out what the mistake is. I correct it. They pay no attention whatsoever.

That is sin.

Nothing that has ever happened down there has delighted me more than Noah and his ark.

The old gentleman *was,* as we know, a bit of a drinker, but like so many drinkers kindly, compassionate, and in a fey sort of a way, creative. To be sure the stuff had addled his wits to the point where he greatly exaggerated the rainfall. Four days would be more like it, and the floods, while impressive, certainly didn't cover the whole earth. How he managed to confuse Mount Ararat with the whole continent of Africa, however, is more than I can comprehend. The H.G., masquerading as one of his dumb doves, contributed not a little to the confusion, and playful Esther, disporting herself around that pathetic parody of an ocean liner, supported the grotesque illusion.

Imagine, though, one mad old man determined to rescue the entire animal kingdom from what he fancied to be extinction! I must say I prefer his fantasy to their relentless extinction of the animals for the care of which I specifically entrusted them. Defunct as the dodo is the naïveté of Noah. Nothing more precious was lost in that petulant flood. Noah survived, and with him the animals, but the innocence jettisoned in the garden was drowned in extravagant tides.

What a sight it was! As Myrtle said: "It looks like a box of animal crackers someone carelessly dropped into Niagara Falls." Not even Walt Disney could have dreamed up such an improbable adventure. P. T. Barnum, had he seen it, would have folded his tents and turned sucker himself.

All in all, it was one of mankind's better moments.

A word about earthquakes.

I am sick and tired of being blamed for earthquakes. I do not, could not, would not, have not, and will not cause earthquakes! It would be entirely out of character. I'd be much more likely to knock the bottom out of the stock market.

Once and for all: I did make earth; it happens to be one property of earth now and then to quake; that is all there is to it.

Bishop Pike doesn't bother me a bit.

Sure, he says some pretty irreverent things, especially when speaking off the cuff, but I can take all he gives out and give him back a few lumps he won't soon forget. I certainly prefer his frolicsome impertinence to the simpering, servile, unctuous obsequies most bishops direct at me.

His books bother me. Too hastily dashed off. Can't the man sit down for a month and do the job right? Mind you, I've read everything he's done, and enjoyed myself mightily. If I have to read their so-called theology I'd rather read the Bishop than Maritain; I might not agree with him, but at least I understand what he's talking about.

But how can they call him a heretic, of all things Perhaps it's because he insists on thinking and saying what he thinks—sometimes the other way around—which *is* a peculiar compulsion for a bishop. Heretic, shmeretic! The man's got enthusiasm. *I* think they're out to get him because he enjoys his work. For my part, I think of him as a sort of holy horsefly. No doubt they'll shake him off, one way or another, and lumber sluggishly on into further sloughs of fatuity.

Frankly, I can hardly wait for him to get up here—and if he doesn't slow down I won't have long to wait. He'll definitely be a regular at my Saturday night stags. I like good conversation. I like good company. I like a man who thinks for himself.

I *like* Bishop Pike.

Well, now I've heard everything.

There's a lady psychiatrist down there who has concocted the notion that the H.G. is a woman!

This lady—Margaretta Bowers; Dr. Bowers, I should say—specializes in the treatment of priests and that may be the root of her speculation. Her argument has some merit. She says that I—as Love—could not deny equal rights to women in the highest places. (She doesn't know about Myrtle, of course, or Esther, both of whom have *un*equal rights around here, so far as I can make out.) She also claims that the church by suppressing the H.G.'s femininity has fostered a compensatory phenomenon called the Cult of Mary. That seems a bit farfetched to me, but who am I to say?

The truth of the matter is I don't know for a fact what sex, if any, the H.G. has. I never think of him—it?—in such connections. When would he find the time? I almost asked him this morning, but I couldn't bring myself to do it. He would have been *so* embarrassed! No matter what way it turned out. If he *is* a woman that would account for some queries I've had in my mind for some ages about certain of his mannerisms. But really what difference does it make? Skeletons are best left in the closets they're put in.

I think I won't pursue the matter.

Let the record show that I may disassociate myself from all enterprises of Dr. Norman Vincent Peale.

I have read his books, tuned into a number of his "sermons," and even viewed his film. What he has to say makes a certain amount of sense. Anyone who wants to be successful, rich, superior, smug, secure, safe, and respectable should, I would think, do exactly as Dr. Peale suggests. Such people should also be prepared to go where camels go who can't squeeze through the needle's eye. *The man has nerve.* I'll say that for him. In *my* name he propagates puerile simplicities Dale Carnegie would blush to utter.

If the man knew how to listen I'd tell him precisely what he should do with his power of positive thinking. But the whole point of it is to close your eyes, stop up your ears, open your mouth, and shout over and over again: "I am popular! I am successful! I am safe!" People will believe anything they tell themselves often enough. Dr. Peale's home remedies are placebos for the incurably indulgent. Nothing he says is thoughtful; nothing he says is positive; nothing he says is powerful.

Celibacy?

The answer is emphatically: No!

The same goes for birth control.

The same goes for abortions.

I want more life.

Give me more life.

Death is the denial of life.

If I hadn't decided I would have more security as God I would have become a poet.

Nothing I can think of would be more fulfilling for someone with creative energy and a gift for self-expression. It isn't useful, of course, and nothing much comes of it, but then what comes of my creation, for that matter? Trouble, a few laughs, and that recurrent feeling that I've run out of material.

My work leaves me little eternity for hobbies, but when I have a twinkling of an eye I like to dash off a few lines, and I must say, they show a certain *je ne sais quoi.* I am, I suppose, what they would call a Sunday poet. J.C. pooh-poohs my stuff, says I should stick to my own last. Rhymes, according to him, are old hat: "Strictly pre-Olympian, Dad; strictly pre-Olympian." I *want* a rhyme in a poem; otherwise, what's the point? Who cares about a lot of gibberish that doesn't even rhyme, makes no sense, and won't scan? When I read their poetry I stick pretty much to your William Shakespeares, your Dantes, your William Wordsworths. Maybe they *are* square, but at least they know what they're doing, and so do I.

Rhyme, of course, doesn't *guarantee* a good poem. Joyce Kilmer's *Trees* rhymes itself silly and it makes *me* treesick. I yield to no man in my fondness for trees—that's why I made so many of them—and it certainly is true that only I *could* have made a tree. But only I could have made a horned lizard. Does that make a horned lizard lovely? I should hope *not.* Mr. Kilmer no doubt means well, but if he fancies I'm flattered he'll find out on TooLateDay just how mistaken he is.

But I agree with Robert Frost. Writing poetry without rhymes is like playing tennis without a net. What do they think I put rhymes in their idiot languages for? To rhyme with, that's what for!

Anyhow, I've done a poem—today is Sunday—and I do honestly believe it's one of my best. Bear in mind, I don't profess to be

37

a professional, merely an accomplished amateur. My poem does rhyme. It scans. It has a message *and* a moral. It does not strain for its effects. And it has a lot of me in it—the *real* me—a sort of *divination* of the inscrutable. I know I protest too much, but I'm shy about my poems as I wouldn't be about, say, a plague of locusts. Well, here goes!

A MIRROR IS A MIRROR IS A MIRROR
"Gertrude Stein always sits
with her back to the view."
—A. Toklas

How I wish that I could see
A mirror of eternity;
Nothing there would I discern
Save sands of time Hell couldn't burn:

Daniel's Den and Noah's Ark,
Mr. Olmstead's Central Park,
Marmaduke, the Christian dog,
And fragments of the Decalogue;

Sunset, wave-break, deep sleep, dawn,
Big Ben (Nordberg), good Pope John,
All creation, thanking me,
Eats bread, drinks wine, and toasts J.C.;

Joy's extinguished death's mirage!
Sister Corita's taken charge!
Mirror! Mirror! Help me see
More and more eternity!

For the several "in-jokes" in the poem I must apologize, pleading poetic license and the difficulty, as in the fourth stanza, of rhyming the more obvious. While I do not, as a rule, approve of poets calling attention to their special effects, I hope readers will not overlook how by hyphenating "wave-break" the feeling of a break is subtly accentuated. I cannot stress enough that in any creative undertaking scrupulous concern for detail pays off.

Superstition, contrary to what their theologians proclaim about it, is the highest form of religion as idolatry is the lowest.

To stand above, which is what superstition means, is, after all, what *I* do. Everybody who respects me for that has earned my good will. What care I if at the same time they are misled into supposing that I abhor number 13? How should they be *expected* to know that 69 is the only authentically unlucky number? Trial and error, perhaps, but how many numbers can one person try? Nor am I greatly put off when some sect decides that St. So-and-So's fallen arch will cure chronic Achilles' heel. Faith has moved many an arch up and can make even *heels* invulnerable.

Take Presbyterians. Superstitious as they come! That confession of theirs, which they have revised into gibberish, wholly misses the point! I *just* don't care. I can think offhand of many a splendid Presbyterian, half a dozen easily, and that, as things go down below, is a bonanza. Consider their world director for cities, a most demanding, not to say hopeless, post: noble fellow, quite likely a Christian. I wonder what *he* thinks of the Westminster Confession, as amended? I daresay he doesn't think about it at all.

Idolatry is what I cannot abide! Substitution of some worthless institution for me. Idolatry! Beware all ye who worship banks! or flags! or prayers-in-the-school! or free enterprise! or mothers! or social security! or civil rights! or the John Birch Society! or pot! or law-and-order! or black power! or the immaculate heart of any-thing! *I* am the immaculate heart! Worship me and me alone.

My horoscope this morning was dismaying. Aquarians are advised to keep their opinions to themselves and to avoid intemperate speech.

Their church, I sometimes think, is a monster, gobbling up *my* faithful.

Wrong again, Dr. Aquinas!

(That man makes such a fetish of being reasonable that he completely misses what stares him in the face. A perfectly reasonable man would have to go mad because he would be unable to explain the many irrational elements of my creation. I admire, in that connection, Nathaniel Hawthorne's story *The Birthmark,* which is about a brilliant scientist with a beautiful wife flawed only by a birthmark on her face; the poor fellow ends up killing the lady in a mad attempt to eradicate the blemish. Blemishes are, in fact, marks of beauty, and should be cherished as highlights of the creation.)

It seems that they wonder down there what became of the Garden of Eden after I was obliged to throw that unruly couple out. Legend has it that the original garden lies at the source of the Tigris and Euphrates rivers. Skeptical adventurers went to that source and found no garden at all. Dr. Aquinas—impeccably logical, as ever—accounts for this anomaly by disclosing (without ever having been there himself) that the two rivers flow underground for some distance before arriving at their source. The garden, he says, is actually somewhat farther to the east.

Sorry, my dear sir: 'taint so. *I* answer that:

The Garden of Eden is right where it has always been—some ten miles as the sea gull flies off Point Judith, Rhode Island; roughly forty miles by ferry from the city of Providence (!); perhaps twelve miles due east of Montauk Point, Long Island. An island seven miles by three miles, latterly called, by its inhabitants, Block Island, it is, obviously, the source of no rivers, or, in a sense, surrounded as it is by the sea, the source of all rivers.

It's a lovely spot, gently warmed by the Gulf Stream, terribly chastened by hurricanes, abundant in shrubs, wildflowers, freshwater ponds, hills and vales, sandy beaches, clay cliffs, a haven for birds, spectacular fishes, timid animals. It is, as a matter of fact, the first place in creation I ever set foot on. (The inhabitants have marked the exact spot—on the north shore—with what they whimsically call Settlers' Rock.) I love to walk, and the island has miles and miles of roads and paths and beaches that enjoy being walked on, so I quite often go there to marvel at my creation and, mayhap, to watch a sparrow fall.

The Tree of Knowledge got chopped down ages ago. I remember it well, towering, as it did, over what is called Tilson Cove, enhancing the bluff property now occupied by a poet. How many times I spread myself out under its soothing branches, languidly wondering whether Isaac Newton really knew what hit him. I doubt it. I was furious when they cut it down, compounding their appetite for disobedience with an even grosser appetite for ignorance. But I couldn't bring myself to ruin the island by fitting the punishment to the crime. I contented myself with visiting the place with an extreme paucity of trees, the only evidence on the island of the fallen estate of man.

Since the Fall the island has been fortunate, in the main, in its inhabitants, nearly all of them, I'm pleased to report, Me-fearing. For many a century astonishing Indians lived there, and were, happily, satisfied to preserve the primitive character of the garden as I had originally conceived it. Later, the blah-faced people came, fugitives from decadent civilization. Many of them were frugal, hard-working, orderly folk who left their mark on the island in miles and miles and miles of charming stone walls. It's as though they knew the original spontaneous order of the garden had been forever lost and wished to pay their respects to that order by making a pattern not even disorder could abridge. When I look at it I am almost persuaded that they have succeeded.

Anyhow, Dr. Aquinas, should you wish to inform yourself *accurately* on the post-Fall history of the Garden of Eden, I respectfully refer you to: S. T. Livermore's (The Rev.) HISTORY OF BLOCK ISLAND, Rhode Island. Originally printed 1877; reproduced and enhanced by The Block Island Committee of Republication for The Block Island Tercentenary Anniversary, 1961. Printed by facsimile, with addenda, by The Murray Printing Company, Forge Village, Massachusetts. Library of Congress No. 61–17173: Price $2.50.

". . . . . , God willing."

Now *there's* a phrase, commonplace below, worth pondering.
What in the name of Osiris does it mean? They say things to each
other like: "See you tomorrow, God willing." Why should I be
unwilling? Suppose that for some curious reason I *might* be unwilling, what do they suppose I could do about it? Stick pins in a
wax doll? When that Joshua caused the sun to stand still—about
which I certainly *was* unwilling—what could I do? Not a thing.
And it was some mess, I'll tell you, trying to get the celestial
system back in shape. (The big dipper leaks to this instant; and the
devil take it, it can leak forever, for all I care.) I may be
omnipotent but I'm not an idiot!

Imagine, for the sake of argument, a family of them all set for
the annual outing. The car is crammed with junk inside, backside,
topside; the kiddies squirm wretchedly in the back seat; poppa is
enthroned behind the wheel; mommy, puppy in her lap, nervously
eyes the milkman's note. Now, would poppa say, cheerily: "Well,
here we go, Henry Ford willing"? Of course not. Either the car will
work or it won't. Henry Ford can't make it go, and Henry Ford
can't make it not go. And if Henry Ford can't make a car go, how
in the name of Mercury do they expect me to?

Even the H.G. is addicted to the phrase. He's in and out of my
office half a dozen times a day with lurid accounts of some war or
orgy or heresy or what have you. Invariably he concludes his
breathless horror story with the same preposterous importunity:
"For J.C.'s sake, *do* something!" Do what? *That's* what I want to
know.

David and Goliath.

That is what I think of when I brood about their churches. On one hand, you have vast, rich, empty, ugly, and pretentious cathedrals; on the other hand, you have tiny, poor, overflowing, lovely, and unassuming store-front churches. In the cathedrals the world itself sits enthroned; in the little churches faith empties itself out improvidently.

J.C. would not be let in any of their cathedrals; he will not wear a necktie. He adores, on the other hand, three churches in New York City: Judson Memorial Church in Greenwich Village, where even artists can get in and people have been known to smoke during services; St. Mark's in the Bowery, where they may smoke pot for all I know; and Chambers Memorial Baptist Church in East Harlem, which has a minister who believes not only in me but even in J.C.

The H.G. frequently commends to me another New York City church, on Fifth Avenue, which has an enormous endowment that is managed, the H.G. says, more impeccably than the portfolio of the Metropolitan Life Insurance Company! The church's rector often admonishes his flock to up their annual ante lest he be compelled to dip into capital. Verily I say unto that misguided rector: *"Your* capital, Reverend Sir, will not squeeze you through *my* needle's eye." In the bargain basement below, however, His Horny-tailed Nibs will no doubt find multiple uses for so much hoarded cash: a new fiery furnace, perhaps, or a swanky billiard parlor for versatile confidence men.

Goliath may prosper but David will prevail.

I must make a note to tell Myrtle to dock J.C.'s allowance again.

His little pranks may be amusing, but he does get carried away.

With due respect for the exuberance of youth, a certain discipline has to be exercised or the example he sets will be woefully distorted. Like when he was barely old enough to fly a kite and toddled into that temple and stumped all the wise men with his precocious prattle. The truth is any child could have done that to any wise man. But J.C. isn't *any* child; he is my only son in whom I try to be well pleased. Mary—if you want to know what I think—should have turned the lad over her knee and given him a good thrashing. But Mary always was too soft on him. Spoiled him, if you really want to know what I think. And Joseph! Nice fellow, I grant you, but frankly I sometimes wonder. Well, the damage is done; no use brooding about it.

What has he done now? Well, he was wandering around with that crowd of goof-offs he calls his "bunch," attracting a lot of public attention and generally making a nuisance of himself. (He *does* have leadership potential, I notice, and he'll sure need it.) Somehow or other he got separated from the rest of them, who went out to sea for some fishing. So J.C., nothing daunted, got Esther into the surf, climbed on her back, and off they went in hot pursuit. Now, when old Esther pulled alongside the others with J.C. nonchalantly aloft I want you to know that slovenly crew sat up and took notice! They were like to die! And I can't say I blame them. I must say I never thought J.C.'s surfboarding would achieve anything, but it sure came in handy today.

Nonetheless! The lad must learn restraint. Don't you just know that in no time they will be saying he walked on water? *I* know it. And from that harmless bit of misinformation they will leap to such conclusions as you wouldn't believe possible. J.C. should *stop and think* before he goes off halfcocked! Therefore: five loaves, two fish—current allowance; three loaves, one fish—probationary allowance. He'll just have to stretch that as best he can. It's time he learned the value of loaves and fishes, anyhow. The way he throws the stuff around you'd think they grew on trees.

Eleven o'clock Sunday morning is the most segregated hour in the American week.

Truer words were never spoken.

Their churches might as well hang "White only" (or "Black only") signs on the altar and be done with it. Who do they think they're kidding with their pronouncements? Not me, I can tell you. For every clergyman they've got who'll put his cross on the line there are fifty who wouldn't cross the street to comfort the good Samaritan. Hang their hypocrisy! I repudiate the lot of them.

Wars will end when there are more atheists in foxholes; racism will end when there are fewer collars turned backwards in pulpits. Most clergymen look in the same direction their collars point. Let them look, blast them, at what stares them in the face. They might begin by consulting a mirror. Failing that, I commend the New Testament. Failing that, let them look at the faces in their congregations. They cannot fail to notice that those faces also stare in the direction the backward collars point. People who wish to look ahead have no time to sit in uncomfortable pews parsing the *Articles of Religion*.

"Forward-pointing collars only." *That* is the sign I would hang on their altars.

Work! Work! Work!

That's what it all adds up to.

One thing I've always wanted to do, but it will never happen because the network, typically, tossed the show off the air.

I would *love* (not to debase a basic word) to go on *What's My Line?* They would *never* get it! Mr. Cerf would be stumped; he might even be speechless. Miss Francis would lose her false eyelashes along with her spooky mask. I would have *a* ball!

Can't you hear them? "Is it bigger than a breadbox?" (It sure is, my dear.) "Do you come into contact with people in what you do?" (Sooner or later, I do.) "Could I eat your product?" (Many people try.) "Have you ever appeared in films?" (John Houston claims I have.) It would be a gas!

Besides, it wouldn't hurt to make friends with a fellow who married the daughter of the Chief Justice. It pays to have a friend in court, I always say.

Fantasies! Fantasies!

Sometimes I think if I hadn't revealed *anything* to them they would have worked it all out much more sensibly.

I see nothing wrong with their passion to get to the bottom of things, but why do they have to make dogmas out of what they find there? Especially when what they find is usually either obvious, trivial, or absurd.

For example: Mary, they proclaim, was, when J.C. was conceived, a virgin. Well, I should hope *so!* Mary was a nice girl, after all. From that astonishing news they press on to the conclusion that her unique chore required that she should have been without sin when she herself was conceived. *That* they solemnly call Immaculate Conception. Since everyone else is without sin when conceived, why not Mary? But why a dogma? Who in the name of Astarte would bother to doubt it? Not content with that, however, poor old Pius XII decided it was incumbent upon the faithful to believe that dear Mary was bodily assumed into heaven. Granted the old martinet was senile and the strains of a long pontificate are corrosive. But just how otherwise could she have been assumed? The only ghost I've got around this place is the H.G., and even he's got a body, sparse though it may be. The very last thing that sweet, unassuming (if I may put it that way) lady wants is worship, and she certainly knows little and cares less about their mariology.

But it was about their so-called doctrine of original sin that I meant to complain. What twaddle! Can't they find enough sin all around them without trying to discover an *original* sin? The only original sin I can conceive of is the mistake of getting born in the first place, which is more than canceled out by later on dying—terminal sin, so to speak.

J.C. gets on so well with artists.

They always make *me* uncomfortable. I have the feeling they are reproaching me as if I didn't really do the creation right. Not that they could have done any better. But they *think* they could have. And then, what do you *say* to an artist? If you say the weather is pleasant, he'll tell you the light is bad for his work. If you say he's looking well, he'll say appearance doesn't interest him. If you say you're happy to see him, he'll ask why.

J.C. doesn't try to talk to them. He listens. They flock around him like little children around a calliope. I suppose he is what they call attractive. But appearance, they say, doesn't interest them. What could it be? I don't know. Maybe they just like his style.

Sometimes I think I'm losing my grip.

Sunday is the biggest mistake I ever made. I figured I was entitled to one day of my very own, a day of rest. Rest! Ha! What have they made of it? They have made it a day devoted to tormenting *me*. On Sundays nothing—not even Mozart played at top volume on my stereo console—can drown out their infernal church choirs. And their offertory soloists! Angels and ministers of death deliver me! At least the Quakers have the decency to keep quiet. What do they think I am? I have news for the lot of them, and the news isn't good. God is not an acoustical ceiling.

My hypostasis is acting up again. Nothing seems to help. Time was I could settle it very nicely with an hour in the sauna, or even a short nap. Now it's got to the point where Seconal won't work and whole centuries of nights go by without a single wink of sleep. I have even considered praying. But to whom? The cloud of unknowing enfolds me and me alone. The buck, as Mr. Truman said, stops here. And I mean it *really* stops here. I would give my omniscience to be able to pass just one decision on to higher authority.

The trouble all started when they began telling me I was actually three persons. Utter nonsense, I know, but once the notion got planted I couldn't help wondering if maybe I *am* three persons. I would find myself muttering: "I am that I am that I am that I am." Sometimes I would hear myself say to myself: "Behave yourself or I'll have to speak to yourself about yourself." A line of T. S. Eliot's got lodged in my head (s?): ". . . distracted from distraction by distraction . . ." *That,* my dear Dr. Aquinas, is what it feels like to *be* trinitarian.

The Holy Ghost—blast his wretched sense of humor!—has invented a name for my affliction: *hypostatic schizophrenia.* J.C., on the other hand, was more consoling. "Dad," said he, "be glad they didn't decide you were half bull." The dear lad doesn't know that whole eternities go by when I'm not sure in my own mind I'm not *all* bull.

Be that as it may, some of my mes have to go. One of me is all I can bear.

Let me clear up one point. *Grape juice will not work*. Furthermore, the vintage and bouquet of the wine are both important. Any wine *might* work, but you're a whole lot safer with, say, a *Saint-Émilion,* 1964. (The H.G. tells me he's had reports of successful results in several cases with cooking sherry, but the H.G. grasps, sometimes, at straws.) White wine, assuming a decent vintage, is just as good as red. Champagne, for example, is almost foolproof. There is most definitely no efficacy whatever unless the wine is personally drunk.

Sadly I have to say brandy is deceptive. You will think it did work but discover on TooLateDay that it didn't.

The bread needs to be home-baked. Store-bought bread is hopeless. Absence of leaven *apparently* is slightly preferable, but I myself don't feel the difference justifies the sacrifice in flavor. It's really a matter of taste.

There is no reason not to have a good cheese with it. The cheese has nothing to do with the efficacy, but I find it goes down better that way, and it appeases the dairy folks.

A true flower of my church (that vast wasteland of tares and thistles) is good Pope John.

What a joy to have him here! What a pity he couldn't have lingered below a bit longer!

An orotund breath of fresh air, here or there, that's what the old fellow is. When he arrived I at once received him in private audience, the first such dispensation I have granted since the arrival of St. Thomas More. Not even my omniscience had prepared me for his first words: "Do you mind, Sir, if I open a window?" He plays a stalwart hand of bezique and has a fine appreciation of the wines of Frascati, which I had never really given a chance until he commended them.

Marvin Halverson, a guest tonight for the first time at my regular Saturday stags, passed along a story about John that I hadn't happened to hear before. It seems the old Pope was strolling down a corridor of the Vatican Palace in the company of two aides when, suddenly, out of the corner of his eye he spotted J.C. sitting in a side chapel. "Looka-busy, looka-busy," said the Pope; "he's-a-come back, he's-a-come back!" I suppose the story's apocryphal, but it shouldn't be.

I hope they don't turn him into a saint; he's much too lovable for that.

I've kept my Saturday night stags strictly off the record to encourage maximum freedom of conversation. Besides, they're nobody's business anyway. How I look forward to them! The only few hours each week when I can let down what hair I've got and be myself.

The formula is as inflexible as it is simple. A superb basic dinner with excellent wines, coffee, music, and talk, talk, talk! There are few flaws. The H.G. *will* drink milk with his dinner and he *will* plod grimly through an interminable shaggy dog tale. And I do wish J.C. would come more often even if he does find the whole thing a "drag." Myrtle *will* break in at some point with an "urgent" message that could just as well have waited. She *must* know who the special guests are so she can gossip all over empyrean about them.

Always there are twelve guests—the eight "steadies" and four "oncers"—making a comfortable thirteen at table. Each evening centers around a particular subject which determines who the "oncers" will be. The "steadies," all (with the exception of the H.G.) eminently civilized, are:

the H.G.	Dr. Freud
J.C./or King David	Karl Marx
Paul	Gov. Stevenson
Socrates	John XXIII

The H.G. invariably sits to my left, J.C. (or King David) of course to my right; otherwise guests seat themselves as they see fit. Oddly, Paul always makes a beeline for second to the right, and John always sits at the left-side foot of the table. The others don't seem to care where they sit, nor do I. The H.G., by unfortunate custom, says grace. (I do wish he'd find something more couth than: "Thanks be to God we can afford.") During dinner we banter back and forth topical events of the day, here, there, and elsewhere, stressing wit and anecdote. The only serious note creeps in over dessert when the rest of us tolerate a knockdown/ drag-out between Paul and Karl on community organization. Each of them has a valid point, but I quit ages ago trying to reconcile them. As the Governor put it: "It would be easier to hammer a thought into General Eisenhower's skull, or, having done it, to dig it out again." Pity, I think, those fools didn't have sense enough to let Adlai have a go at it.

I did consider, by the way, including women—J.C. suggested it—but after aeons of reflection the only woman I could think of who would really fit in was Mrs. Franklin D. Roosevelt, and she doesn't drink. So, I decided instead to set aside Thursday lunch for the great lady, and I've never regretted it. (I have a glass of *vin rosé*; she has tea.) That woman has taught me more about politics than I could have picked up in half an eternity at Yale.

Now as to how the "oncers" work. Well, tonight, for example, I thought the time had come to chew over their so-called "just war" theory. I never have understood it, instinctively deplore it, and specifically deny I have ever supported *any* war, or any *side* in any war, but I nonetheless believe in *hearing* all sides. So, for this occasion the "oncers" were:

St. Augustine	Montezuma
Richard the Lion-hearted	A. J. Muste

Notice that the guests were carefully balanced to insure a fair presentation of the pros and the cons of the issue. (Montezuma, incidentally, was utterly charming. He brought me a lovely, pure gold cummerbund, handsomely inlaid with precious stones, that I'm almost sure is pre-Columbian!) Well, I want you to know we had a real go-around over coffee. I still don't see how a war can be just, but I do see how someone less than omniscient might *think* a war could be just. There *was* Genghis Khan. There *was* Napolean. There *was* Hitler. There's no getting around it that something had to be done. You could have turned all the cheeks on earth at any one of the beasts and gotten nowhere. No use telling them, I fear, that anyone who insists on being peaceful is indestructible. How do they know until they've tried it? Mr. Muste knows because he did try it. It *is* reassuring to find, once in a fuchsia moon, a man who listened to what I said, acted accordingly, and found, sure as an unshot gun, that it worked. War is a despicable fraud!

The conversation did get acrimonious, alas; but with such a subject, how could it have been otherwise? We talked some, for example, about that American war in Vietnam, which *is,* as Mr. U Thant said, one of the most "barbarous" in all war's wretched history. John wondered, absently it seemed to me, how a Cardinal could have lent his princely prestige to such a monstrous abomination. It was Augustine, as I recall, who responded: "Because he knows a just war when he sees one." To which the H.G.—somewhat to my surprise—rejoindered: "I don't trust that man's cherubic smile!" I will not have anyone preaching victory in war on J.C.'s birthday! Even so I do wish the H.G. could have expressed his point more delicately.

Anyhow, after a spirited discussion—we went well past midnight —I took a poll, as now and then I do when the subject is unresolved, and the result may be of some inconclusive interest. I voted last, as is my habit, so as not to prejudice the outcome. The tabulation, as I discovered it on the back of Governor Stevenson's bezique score when I was picking up this morning:

	Anti-just-war	*pro-just-war*	*abstained*
	the H.G.		
		King David*	
			Paul
			Socrates
		Dr. Freud	
	Karl Marx		
	Gov. Stevenson		
	John XXIII		
		St. Augustine	
		Richard the L.	
	Montezuma		
	A. J. Muste		
Totals	6	4	2
God:	1		
	7	4	2

* J.C. had a previous engagement, and couldn't make it.

67

Is the Pope infallible?

Am I omnipotent?

Yes and No.

Do angels exist or don't they?

More pseudoscholarly rot has been uttered below on that curious subject than has been written on the question of who wrote Shakespeare. It's a perfect example of an end I shaped precisely, only to sit helpless above while they roughhew it to suit themselves.

If angels did not exist I would have to invent them, which comes, perhaps, to the same thing. What more can I say?

Fulton Sheen recovered from his halitosis of the soul.

No, my dear Lady Bird!

There is nothing beautiful about beautification. You may have noticed that cosmetics are no substitute for the real thing. You can plant all the hollyhocks you want on the fringes of city dumps, but the dumps will remain.

Scatter ye rosebuds while ye may. But rosebuds don't last. Dumps do. Tell your husband to stop dumping. That would be more to the point. And he might begin by stopping the dumping of bombs on North Vietnam and napalm on South Vietnam.

Beauty is *not* in the eye of the beholder. Beautification is.

This morning I granted one of my infrequent general press conferences.

Ordinarily, when I have something momentous to reveal, I prefer to leak it to someone of stature—*a* Jude the Obscure, *a* Gautama Buddha, *a* Friedrich Nietzsche, *a* Walter Lippmann—but today I found, somewhat ominously, that I had nothing on my mind I hadn't already said somewhere before. I merely wanted to put to rest all the wild rumors circulating about my health: that I have failed badly in recent aeons, that my doctors have placed me in strict quarantine, even—so help me—that I am already dead! To cope with all that I decided upon maximum multimedia exposure.

To establish a suitably low-keyed atmosphere I first of all deftly fielded several questions on the subject of birth control. (They're not about to impale me on *that* sticky wicket.) Having provoked a decorous merriment, I then moved at once to the matter at hand:

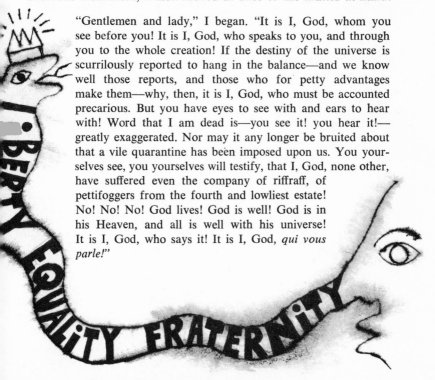

"Gentlemen and lady," I began. "It is I, God, whom you see before you! It is I, God, who speaks to you, and through you to the whole creation! If the destiny of the universe is scurrilously reported to hang in the balance—and we know well those reports, and those who for petty advantages make them—why, then, it is I, God, who must be accounted precarious. But you have eyes to see with and ears to hear with! Word that I am dead is—you see it! you hear it!— greatly exaggerated. Nor may it any longer be bruited about that a vile quarantine has been imposed upon us. You yourselves see, you yourselves will testify, that I, God, none other, have suffered even the company of riffraff, of pettifoggers from the fourth and lowliest estate! No! No! No! God lives! God is well! God is in his Heaven, and all is well with his universe! It is I, God, who says it! It is I, God, *qui vous parle!*"

So that there should be no question whatever that I am in full possession of my faculties I spoke deliberately, calmly—with an economy of ample gestures—and, of course, without notes. (I was up most of the night listening to myself over and over again on tape until not a single inflection was awry. And a good thing, too, since I stupidly forgot to bring my spectacles along this morning.) Immediately, I rose and strode with vigor and detachment from the hall, exiting to prolonged and agitated applause. It was an impressive performance.

Myrtle thereupon distributed copies of the last medical reports on my state of health. Nothing was left out. I have nothing to hide, nothing to conceal. I am in excellent health, the reports indicate, for a god of my age. I am a touch too heavy. I need to get more rest than I normally do. There is some tenderness of the *omnipotens,* nothing alarming. Everything else checks out just fine. There *was* one somewhat disconcerting conclusion—let's hope the press doesn't pick it up—having to do with what the doctors called "preliminary symptoms of a *possible slight* diminishing influence, a condition that must be watched." Doctors always find some reason to keep me worried; otherwise I would stop consulting them. One thing is certain: I never felt better in my existence!

Wouldn't you know, though, that the conference was barely over when I was handed a note from Harrison Salisbury: "Would you be kind enough to let the *Times* know the moment your health *does* fail?" I replied in my own hand at once: "I did not, sir, become God in order to preside over my own demise, least of all prematurely!" That should hold him.

I certainly never wanted to be called anything so awful as Jehovah.

But I must say I prefer Jehovah to Yahweh.

This afternoon the H.G. was overdoing, as usual, his "Your Excellency" this, "Your Excellency" that, bit, and suddenly my composure snapped. "Would you, please," I blurted out, "in the name of Quetzalcoatl, just call me God?"

As a confirmed bachelor I have to say I have difficulty fathoming man's preoccupation with woman.

To be sure, I meant that women should be amusing, as very often they are. But I certainly never intended that they should sit *on* thrones or *in* cabinets. That they would chop up saloons strikes me as a perversion of my creation. It never entered my head that they would be allowed to exercise the vote. A woman's place *is* in the home, and if I had my way—and Venus knows I don't—they would confine their women to the kitchen, the nursery, and, of course, the bedroom. Margaret Chase Smith is a splendid lady, but can she make a chocolate mousse? (I do enjoy that story about Mrs. Smith. It seems she was asked what she would do if she woke up some morning and found herself in the White House. "I would apologize to Mrs. Truman, and go home," said she. Which testifies to her respect for a fine example of womanhood, her Yankee wit, and her sense of where she really belongs.) Women are an enigma wrapped in sheer nerve.

Beautiful as she was, Eve was invidiously sly. She knew from the outset that without clothes women would get nowhere. Even a figleaf is provocative, I suppose, pre*fig*uring, as it does, the wanton abondon of the miniskirt. Out of one superfluous rib I created—inadvertently—Twiggy. Not that Eve could be said to have had a *figure,* exactly. She resembled a cobra with an apple for a head. The H.G. insists she had a winning smile. He must be right. She won.

J.C. has always maintained that things would have turned out much better if I had put a lemon on that tree instead of an apple. Could be. But hindsight, I always say, is to foresight what apple-sauce is to apples. Or, as a veteran sinner puts it: "The wages of sin is inconvenience." He can say that again!

What, J.C. wanted to know at lunch, is Arminianism? I explained that it was something Methodists believed because Calvin didn't which produces an aversion to alcohol and tobacco. "What a hang-up," said he. "I hope you're not letting any of *them* up here." To tell the truth (I can do no other), I *am* rather choosy about Methodists, especially the American variety, largely because they are so dead serious about the dullest subjects. (If I hear one more of them say cleanliness is next to godliness I may give up baths altogether.) The Wesley brothers tell me, though, that there's a young Methodist preacher down there now that I should keep an eye on, one Ed Kale; apparently he understands the New Testament, which, if true, would be a major breakthrough, the more so since he is a survivor of the Yale Divinity School.

J.C. likes to say a fellow should live his religion, not run off at the mouth about it all day long. Allowing for the rationalization involved there, I must say he seems to have a point.

"Consider the lilies of the field, how they grow."

O.K. But that's where *I* get lost. I know the line's lovely. I told J.C. so the first time he used it. But what the horny-tailed deuce does it mean? I *know* how the lilies of the field grow. I *grew* them, after all. But what does that leave to *consider?*

I have the same problem with Lord Byron. "Childe Harold to the Dark Tower came." A very fetching image. But *who* is Childe Harold, and *why,* for the love of Lucifer, *did* he to the Dark Tower come? Why, for that matter, couldn't he just *come* to the Dark Tower? I know I have the imagination of an executive. I know H.G. is right when he says J.C. is the *real* poet around this place. But things have to mean *something,* or what's a heaven for?

Jonathan Swift told me at one of my stags that "cellardoor" is the most beautiful word in the English language. He should know, but you couldn't prove it by me. Aeons ago a limpid young poet turned up here with a line of his own devising which he claimed was the loveliest line in the English language: "A long, low line of land." It *is* pretty, I guess. But what could it possibly mean?

In desperation I put the problem of the lilies squarely to J.C. His reply:

"Let's just say, Dad, it's my definition of flower-power." *Now,* where am I?

Who is William Stringfellow?

This morning at my general audience there must have been fifty banners reading: WILLIAM STRINGFELLOW SAVES SIN-NERS. So help me if they have unleashed another evangelist I'll throw in the towel. Strange name, though, for an evangelist. William Stringfellow. The name would suit an actor. I wonder if it's his real name. I wonder, that is, who he is. He must have *charisma*. Maybe he has sex appeal. Well, whoever he is, if he ever turns up, I'd like to have a chat with him. Could it be this is just another of J.C.'s tricks?

I heard today a marvelously Anglican story.

It seems there was a certain bishop, ripe in years and possessed of that aura of authority only bishops can project. A wealthy communicant of his diocese passed on—in this direction, I assume. His funeral was appointed for 3:00 P.M. of such-and-such a day, and since he left much money to the diocese, the Bishop himself consented to officiate at the service. A large congregation gathered in the small country church where the service was to be held, and 3:00 P.M. having come and gone, but no bishop, the young rector determined, rashly, to proceed himself. Down the aisle he strode, proclaiming, after the Episcopal use, "I am the Resurrection and the Life . . ." That was as far as he got. From the rear of the tiny church there boomed out in resonant tones: "Oh, no, young man. *I* am the Resurrection and the Life . . .".

What better proof could there be for the validity of the apostolic succession?

Take the Tower of Babel, for an example. Viewed under the aspect of eternity (as they would say) or from my point of view (as I would say), the edifice has no particular *location*—no time, no place—but is permanent, as audacity is permanent, and it is audacity in the tower that I both marvel at and deplore. To me it appears as a reel of film would appear to them, endlessly unwinding. It is always the same tower, but relentlessly scrutinized it does disclose subtle variations in structure, in hints I discern as to the inhabitants, etc., etc., etc. It is, I might say, a slice of death. The dialogue of the film is utterly unintelligible because I was compelled to scramble their languages to frustrate their audacity, to prevent them from building right through the floor of the empyrean. Our zoning forbids high-rise construction of any kind. The H.G. considers the tower a dreadful bore, and I must say it *is* monotonous, but that, after all, is the point. Take the Tower of Babel, for an example. Viewed under the aspect of eternity (as they would say) or from my point of view (as I would say), the edifice has no particular *location*—no time, no place—but is permanent, as audacity is permanent, and it is audacity in the tower that I both marvel at and deplore. To me it appears as a reel of film would appear to them, endlessly unwinding. It is always the same tower but relentlessly scrutinized it does disclose subtle variations in structure, in hints I discern as to the occupants, etc., etc., etc. It is, I might say, a slice of death. The dialogue of the film is utterly unintelligible because I was compelled to scramble their languages to frustrate their audacity, to prevent them from building right through the floor of the empyrean. Our zoning forbids high-rise construction of any kind. The H.G. considers the tower a dreadful bore, and I must say it *is* monotonous, but that, after all, is the point. Take the Tower of Babel, for an example. Viewed under the aspect of eternity (as they would say) or from my point of view (as I would say), the edifice has no particular *location*—no time, no place—but is permanent, as audacity is permanent, and it is audacity in the tower that I both marvel at and deplore. To me it appears as a reel of film would appear to them, endlessly unwinding. It is always the same tower but relentlessly scrutinized it does disclose subtle variations in structure, in hints I discern as to the occupants, etc., etc., etc. It is, I might say, a slice of death. The dialogue of the film is utterly unintelligible because I was compelled to scramble their languages to frustrate their audacity to prevent them from building right through the floor of the empyrean. Our zoning forbids high-rise construction of any kind. The H.G. considers the tower a dreadful bore, and I must say it *is* monotonous, but that, after all, is the point. Take the Tower of Babel, for an example. Viewed under the aspect of eternity (as

I am often asked to describe a typical day in the life of God, and I may as well do it before Jim Bishop makes a book (and another million) out of it.

I rise betimes at 3:00 A.M., squeeze my own orange juice while the coffee drips, and tune in for a time on early devotions from below. (Their early devotions tend to be more sincere, if sometimes a trifle saccharine.) Ten minutes on the exercycle and then work, work, work! Until 8:00 A.M. I review petitions, memos from the H.G., cables from all over, plan the menus for the day, throw the budget even further out of kilter, dictate for Myrtle, and generally get a jump on things. I like to be two steps ahead, otherwise in no time I'm an aeon behind.

Following a light breakfast with J.C., if he's up, I take Esther for a walk, or in fair weather a swim, garden a bit, have my first

cigarette of the day, and then more work, work, work! The H.G. at 10:00 sharp—always a headache, so I like to get it out of the way; Myrtle at 10:30; Peter at 10:45 (new arrivals); at 11:00 the general audience; 11:45 the mansionkeeper (What I'm going to do about housekeeping expenses I do not know: there are too many

bloody mansions in this house!); at noon the medicine for my *omnipotens,* and one hand of patience.

Lunch is always at 1:00 and always one guest. Guests vary as the universal situation dictates, but Tuesday is held for J.C., Thursday for Mrs. Roosevelt, and Saturday for W. Somerset Maugham. I insist on a leisurely and tasty lunch. Perhaps a light fish, a tossed salad, a suitable wine, cheese, coffee, sometimes a brandy. No matter what the weather, lunch is served on the terrace off my office, overlooking the deep. I love to watch the deep, especially during a storm, when it is tempest-tossed and gong-tormented and the mystery of my creation seems almost to rage back at me. I find it exhilarating.

Directly lunch is over I nap, and no catnap either: I mean I go to bed and sleep until 4:00. Thereupon, the sauna, the pool, and a short walk in the solarium. From 5:00 until dinner I quench my thirst by thumbing through periodicals, private correspondence, or the Sears & Roebuck catalogue.

Dinner (steak, salad, a red wine, coffee) I always take alone (except, of course, for my Saturday night stags). No one can possibly imagine the awesome loneliness of my lofty office! After dinner there is invariably work to be done, which I try to complete before midnight. The last chore of the day is to put down these few words for posterity. Most nights I read myself to sleep, but it is not unusual to find the clock at 3:00 A.M. and I am still turning pages or counting lambs of God as they cavort blissfully on the fields of my infinite mercy.

Christmas again!

It seems to come so often. J.C. certainly has a following. Nobody, I notice, ever makes a fuss over *my* birthday.

What in the name of Nicholas will I get him this time? What, in short, do you get for the kid who's got everything?

Duty compels me to read the whole of their vast church press.

Nothing depresses me more, with the possible exception of my annual audit of their Sunday school curricula materials. I used to read all of that, too, but now the H.G. handles it—he probably enjoys it—and weeds out what he calls "representative theology for tiny tots." Theology, schmeology! Bunkum, that's what it is. Small wonder most of the little monsters grow up to be bigots, boobs, or babbits. I would no more have put J.C. in a Sunday school than I would have put myself on a board of deacons.

But I wander. Most of their church press is so innocuous it isn't even worth denouncing. But I must warn whatever remains of my faithful never to read denominational monthlies, diocesan or parish newsletters, publications of ecumenical bureaucracies, and above all, weekly church bulletins. To do so is literally to suffer the kiss of death. It is simply beyond belief *and*—as a matter of fact—has nothing to do with belief. Eschew, also, any printed matter whatsoever that is placed in pews or on tables at the rear of churches. (Whether or not to eschew as well all envelopes left in similar places, or sent through the mails, I leave to individual discretion.) Whenever I have managed to make my way through several bales of the stuff, I emerge convinced that the massacre of the innocents is sometimes a humdrum affair.

The quality of my judgment, however, is tinged with mercy, and I do wish to commend hesitantly what there is of their religious press that can be ingested without an immediate colic. (Colic, according to Dr. Noah Webster, is: "a paroxysm of acute abdominal pain localized in a hollow organ and caused by spasm, obstruction, or twisting.") It would be prudent to think well of what is written by the religion editors of *The New York Times, Time, Newsweek* and *The San Francisco Chronicle,* especially if you yourself contemplate publishing a book that might fall within their spacious purview. The same might be said of *The Christian Century,* where, additionally, from time to time you may come upon an article of merit or a notable poem. Not to have read, nay subscribed, to *motive,* a magazine of wit, charm, and *élan,* is to have diminished one's chances of survival outside J.C. Any publication that prints anything by Dan Berrigan, S.J., can't be *all* bad. Read, for example, *Ave Maria.* If your liberalism hasn't long since withered on the vine you may be able to drag your way through an occasional issue of *Christianity and Crisis.* Whatever you do, don't fail to read every word of *The Catholic Worker.* I can enthusiastically endorse *Katallagete* (Be Reconciled), the Journal of the Committee of Southern Churchmen. And that, dear children, is *it!* All the rest is opium for the mindless. And not even the mindless will be more than casually comforted.

The H.G. has just come back from another inspection below, and his report is more morose than anything since I had to pull J.C. out after the unpleasantness on the hill.

His assignment was New York City—enough, I vainly supposed, to keep him busy, but wouldn't you know he splashed down in some swamp in Michigan, miles from target area? Not content with having scared a farmer and his wife half out of their wits, he proceeded to chase a state-police patrol car clear through Wisconsin. *That* provoked a whole new wave of flying-saucer reports. (Why they find our extrafirmamental vehicles so perplexing is more than I can understand. How do they expect us to get down there? The H.G. may have a thing about doves, but he's not a carrier pigeon.) I knew I should have sent Gabriel along, but the H.G. wanted to show me he could handle a big job solo. Solo indeed! He couldn't even emanate if J.C. didn't stand beside him reading the

instructions, step by step. I may have to take him out of the field altogether, and confine him indefinitely to desk jobs.

Well, what with the UFO alert, a landing in Central Park was out, of course, so he made a midnight touchdown in the Brooklyn Botanical Gardens, ruining a new planting of hibiscus, changed into a tuxedo with tails, took the subway into Manhattan, missed the Lincoln Center stop, and surfaced grandly at 125th Street and 7th Avenue plumb in the middle of a race riot! Happening to spot some Negro youths plundering a liquor store, he drew himself up to his full five feet two inches, raised his ebony cane imperiously, and commanded: "In the name of God, stop!" They beat him up. Some police attempted to rescue him, but he would have none of it: "Unhand me," said he. When they persisted he shouted: "Police brutality!" So, they hit him over the head with a nightstick, tossed him in the back of a paddy wagon, booked him in night court, and held him three days in the Tombs. (His report reads: "J.C.'s descent into Hell was a *vacation* compared to that experience.") How many times do I have to repeat that even when we are *in* the world we are not *of* it, that we are *strictly* impartial and neutral, and that we do not *ever* engage in social or political action of any kind? Until the heavens boil over, no doubt. The H.G. is incurably meddlesome.

His entrance thereby accomplished, the H.G., bowed but un-bloodied, quietly checked into the Downtown Athletic Club, left his card at Gracie Mansion, lunched with U Thant, placed a wreath at Grant's Tomb, visited the top of the Empire State Building ("I felt I was monarch of all I surveyed"), dropped my order off at Brentano's, picked up a few band concert recordings at Sam Goody's, looked in on the Stock Exchange ("A very well-organized and businesslike institution that many of their churches would do well to emulate"), treated himself to a "swell" dinner at Longchamp's, availed himself of a free ticket to the Ed Sullivan Show, "risked" a champale at Toots Shor's, and retired, pleased to have picked up a "feel" for the city. His satisfaction does not seem to have survived a week, however, since his voluminous report concludes: "It is probably a nice place to live, but it's a devil of a place to visit." Given that his assignment required an inspection of every church in the five boroughs, his disillusionment is understandable.

The report itself is nearly as obtuse as it is verbose, but by reading between the lines I discern that America, for which I had some hopes early on, has gone pretty much berserk. They have turned one of the loveliest landscapes in all creation into a jungle of ugliness. I have given them more than I have given any other people and they have abused my gifts more brutally than has any other people. My sense of humor, which is divine, deserts me. I have known no such wrath since the tribes of Israel violated the particular covenent I made with them. I give them this solemn word: "Cease your destruction and your deprivations; return from throughout the earth to the place I gave you; put your own house in order; clean up the unspeakable mess which you have made. Otherwise, all that you have will be taken from you in calamities and catastrophes and plagues the like of which you cannot even imagine! Not one dollar bill, not one intercontinental missile, not one T-bone steak will survive the wrath you have devised out of my grace!" What do they take me for? Who do they think it is that they mock? I am a very old god, and a very patient god, and my wrath is very terrible.

Well, better I take it out on them than on the poor H.G. At least *he* means well. Perhaps I should invite him to make an oral report at general audience tomorrow. It would make him feel good.

I must try not to lose my temper. After my outburst on reading the H.G.'s New York City report I had the worst flare-up of my *omnipotens* I've had since the Council of Trent.

That might have been endurable, but the doctors insisted on a complete checkup. They concluded that the *omnipotens* would respond to treatment, but they found further signs of that pesky diminishing influence. *What,* I finally worked up the nerve to ask, *is* a diminishing influence? There comes a time, I was told, when even gods must face the passage of eternities, must slow down. "You can't go on forever, you know." Why not? I'm just as fit now as I was in the beginning. My influence, so far as I can tell, is undiminished.

They were even muttering about some surgeon in Atlanta who might be consulted. Altizer, I think the name was.

What fun! Tonight the H.G., J.C., and I got together for one of our old-time religion hymn-sings. I wish they happened more often.

We always lay in a keg of cold draft beer to lubricate the vocal chords. (The H.G. brings his own celery soda.) Our custom is to open with a trio—the H.G. also mutilating the organ—usually: *Praise Us From Whom All Blessings Flow.* (Even old Esther can't stifle a smile when the H.G., with his scratchy falsetto, soars into the concluding: "Praise *Father,* Son *and Holy Me-e-e-e-!"*) We've done *Praise Us* so many times we sound like the three blind mice.

From that we move into what we call the "competitions." Each of us in turn renders solo three hymns that have most irritated us during recent "tune-in duty," that horrid chore one of us has to do every Sunday morning in order to monitor their so-called devotions. Tonight's program was typical, and happily it was noted down by Myrtle, who makes a point of listening through a keyhole:

(J.C.)   *A Mighty Fortress is My Dad*
(H.G.)   *Oh, Come All Ye Faithless!*
(BOSS) *Oh Me, Their Help in Ages Past*
(J.C.)   *Their Eyes Have Seen the Glory of the Coming of J.C.*
(H.G.)   *God Save America*
(BOSS) *Why Save Their Gracious Queen?*
(J.C.)   *Praise J.C., and Pass the Marijuana*
(H.G.)   *Nearer I Could Not Be*
(BOSS) *Now Thank We All for Them*

Some of our lyrics are on the risible side, especially J.C.'s, and I won't set them down here. But we do have fun. It's all in the family—*entre nous*—and it does make it a *little* easier to get through "tune-in duty." Myrtle's notes sum it up: "I laughed so hard the tears ran down my face." And Myrtle isn't easily amused.

Poor Adam Clayton Powell, a fine and funny fellow! He has made himself a dark example of not having your pie and not eating it either.

Reverend Powell fancied he could be a Negro *and* an American. He ends up neither. I will welcome him here because at least he had the sense to know that he had to be either both or neither, not one or the other. He ends up neither. Heaven is filled with *neithers* and Hell is glutted with *one or the others*.

Billy Graham has halitosis of the soul.

Thumbing through miscellaneous issues of *Publishers' Weekly* I must say I do admire those publishers. They landed the Manchester book on John Kennedy—what a joy to have *him* up here!—and then the memoirs of Stalin's daughter, and just about everything by or about Bishop Pike. The next thing you know they'll be after me. And, given a suitable offer, I just might do it. Somewhere, somehow, I am obviously going to have to tell my side of the story.

How I have been misrepresented! How I have been misquoted or quoted out of context! The lies that have been told in my name! I would have to write *volumes* just to set the record straight, and what with my ailments and my responsibilities, when would I ever find the eternity to do it? TooLateDay is very near at hand.

Perhaps the thing is do is to publish my diaries. No. *That* would *really* upset the applecart! *Excerpts* from the diaries. Now there's a thought. But where would I find an editor I could trust? It would require the talents of a poet and the discretion of a saint. Does such an unlikely creature exist?

Disconcerting day! I went, as my doctors insisted, to Atlanta for purely cautionary consultations with Dr. Altizer.

Now he *is* a charming young man. We hit it off at once. We are both great fans of the poetry of William Blake. I happen to prefer "Tiger! Tiger! burning bright . . .," and he goes in more for the later mystical stuff; but at least it established a common bond between us. And he does know his field. What that fellow doesn't know about Hegel *I* don't know about TooLateDay. He *does* have a thing about J.C., but after the way I pushed the lad what can I expect?

He said, for example, that it appears to him that I have *emptied* myself into J.C. (The technical term, if I heard him correctly, is *kenosis*.) He seemed to be hinting that *that* might have something to do with my diminishing influence, if indeed I *have* a diminishing influence. Young men, especially professional young men, tend to leap to conclusions. I have noticed that in J.C.

But that's not what upset me. He insisted on what he called a *battery* of mental tests. *Battery* is the word for it. *So what* if I put the Council of Chalcedon a full century off? What in the name of nepenthe does he expect? I am not the Library of Congress. He *is* a self-assured rascal. Now, it seems, besides the tenderness in the *omnipotens* I am supposed to have aberrations of the *omniscientia*. Where will it all end? I should have stayed in bed.

Men have added many things to my creation, some few that have enhanced it, too much that has debased it, and among the

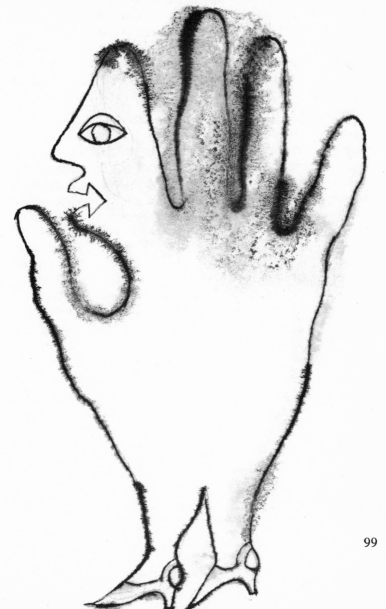

latter nothing, in my sight, has been more execrable than money.

Daily they profligate their souls for tawdry bits of paper and lucred metal. How can they imagine that money has in itself value? One autumn leaf from an oak tree has more value here than all the dollars in Dallas. It is what a thing is, not what it stands for, that gives it value. Money *stands for* an idolatrous and false security, and money *is* an outward and visible manifestation of an inward and unfathomable void. That there is so much money in the world signifies the bankruptcy of mankind. They dare to call it progress! The kingdom I promised them they have sold for a mess of pottage. Money is the incarnation of death.

For the sign of the dollar let them substitute the sign of the cross. The sacrament I ordained for them, the bread and the wine, *is what it stands for,* and *stands for what it is*. It is what it is. But in their fearful distortion they attach to my sacrament the properties of their currency. It is merely a symbol, some say; others fantastically imagine that they are eating and drinking *me!* For the love of Mammon! If I take an aspirin it may bring me relief from pain. That does not mean I am eating relief from pain; I am eating an aspirin and that is all. Whether it does, in fact, relieve my pain depends on many things, including what it is that ails me. On the other hand, the aspirin I eat *is* an aspirin and will do what it will do; there is nothing whatever symbolic about it. But if they *must* distort, I can assure them that my currency is far more solvent than theirs. It is also free of charge.

I had not expected to create my own death, but Dr. Altizer—a regular charmer—leaves me no choice.

My *omnipotens* has, as he puts it, "conked out" completely; my *omniscientia* is failing rapidly; shortly, according to him, I will be *one massive diminishing influence.* That is a humiliation to which I do not choose to submit. I have lost all pride of office, but I trust I retain some dignity of person. Whatever it is I retain shall be devoted to prefiguring a suitable exodus of myself from this pitiful corner into which I have been painted by an ungrateful progeny.

Upon my deathbed I shall linger at least a century. My death will occur just before midnight of November 9, 1965 years after the birth of J.C. I will endure, as an example, an agony of several days, the sedation to be no more than is necessary to kill (forgive the expression) the pain. I will reject the last rites of any church—my death is not a time for discrimination—but will receive, as I suffer out of existence, properly credentialed dignitaries of the faithful. Many children will weep continuously at my bedside.

About an hour before passing on (or *out* or *up* or *down* or wherever it is) I will receive the H.G. alone, but I will be in a coma at the time. Immediately he has fled in consternation I will receive J.C. for ten minutes, also alone. I will yield to him a creation more onerous than any ever devised by deity great or small.

J.C. will withdraw; his last words to me will be: "Have a good trip, Dad!" I will use some few minutes to compose myself for the final ordeal. Suddenly, I will quiver unmercifully, cough weakly but definitively, lift my sunken countenance imperceptibly from the pillow, appear to be about to utter ultimate truth, whereupon I will relax benignly in an attitude of repose.

There will be a dramatic pause.

As I relinquish the ghost I will mutter the words I have so long yearned to repeat:

I am bored with it all.

I always wondered what it would be like.

It does not resemble falling asleep. It is much more like waking up.

Most of all it is like suddenly noticing you have missed your stop on the subway.

I'm glad I did it, but I don't think I'll do it again.

GOD IS DEAD IN GEORGIA

Eminent Deity Succumbs During Surgery—Succession in Doubt As All Creation Groans

LBJ ORDERS FLAGS AT HALF STAFF

Special to The New York Times

ATLANTA, GA., Nov. 9—God, creator of the universe, principal deity of the world's Jews, ultimate reality of Christians, and most eminent of all divinities, died late yesterday during major surgery undertaken to correct a massive diminishing influence. His exact age is not known, but close friends estimate that it greatly exceeded that of all other extant beings. While he did not, in recent years, maintain any fixed abode, his house was said to consist of many mansions.

The cause of death could not be immediately determined, pending an autopsy, but the deity's surgeon, Thomas J. J. Altizer, 38, of Emory University in Atlanta, indicated possible cardiac insufficiency. Assisting Dr. Altizer in the unsuccessful surgery were Dr. Paul van Buren of Temple University, Philadelphia; Dr. William Hamilton of Colgate-Rochester, Rochester, N.Y.; and Dr. Gabriel Vahanian of Syracuse University, Syracuse, N.Y.

Word of the death, long rumored, was officially disclosed to reporters at five minutes before midnight after a full day of mounting anxiety and the comings and going of ecclesiastical dignitaries and members of the immediate family. At the bedside, when the end came, were, in addition to the attending surgeons and several nurses, the Papal Nuncio to the United States, representing His Holiness, Pope Paul VI, Vicar of Christ on Earth and Supreme Pontiff of the Roman Catholic Church; Iakovos, Archbishop of North and South America, representing the Orthodox Churches; Dr. Eugene Carson Blake, Stated Clerk of the Presbyterian Church in the USA, representing the World Council of Churches, predominantly a Protestant institution; Rabbi Mark Tannenbaum of New York City, representing the tribes of Israel, chosen people, according to their faith, of the deceased; The Rev. William Moyers, Baptist minister, representing President Johnson; the 3rd Secretary of the Soviet embassy in Trinidad, representing the Union of Soviet Socialist Republics; and a number of unidentified curious bystanders.

Unable to be in Atlanta owing to the pressure of business at the second Vatican Council, now in session, the

105

Pope, in Rome, said, in part: "We are deeply distressed for we have suffered an incalculable loss. The contributions of God to the Church cannot be measured, and it is difficult to imagine how we shall proceed without Him." Rumors swept through the Council, meeting under the great vaulted dome of St. Peter's, that, before adjourning the Council in December, the Pope will proclaim God a saint, an action, if taken, that would be wholly without precedent in the history of the Church. Several aged women were reported to have come forward with claims of miraculous cures due to God's intervention. One woman, a 103-year-old Bulgarian peasant, is said to have conceived a son at the very instant God expired. Proof of miracles is a precondition for sanctification according to ancient tradition of the Roman Catholic faith.

In Johnson City, Texas, President Johnson, recuperating from his recent gall bladder surgery, was described by aides as "profoundly upset." He at once directed that all flags should be at half-staff until after the funeral. The First Lady and the two presidential daughters, Luci and Lynda, were understood to have wept openly. Luci, 18, the younger daughter, whose engagement has been lately rumored, is a convert to Roman Catholicism. It is assumed that the President and his family, including his cousin Oriole, will attend the last rites, if the international situation permits. Both houses of Congress met in Washington at noon today and promptly adjourned after passing a joint resolution expressing "grief and great respect for the departed spiritual leader." Sen. Wayne Morse, Dem. of Oregon, objected on the grounds that the resolution violated the principle of separation of church and state, but he was overruled by Vice President Hubert Humphrey, who remarked that "this is not a time for partisan politics."

Plans for the deity's funeral are incomplete. Reliable sources suggested that extensive negotiations may be necessary in order to select a church for the services and an appropriate liturgy. Dr. Wilhelm Pauck, theologian, of Union Seminary in New York City proposed this morning that it would be "fitting and seemly" to inter the remains in the ultimate ground of all being, but it is not known whether that proposal is acceptable to the family. Funerals for divinities, common in ancient times, have been exceedingly rare in recent centuries, and it is understood that the family wishes to review details of earlier funerals before settling upon rites suitable for God.

(In New York, meanwhile, the stock market dropped sharply in early trading. Volume was heavy. One broker called it the most active market day since the assassination of President Kennedy, Nov. 22, 1963. The market rallied in late trading, after reports were received that Jesus—see 'Man in the News,' p. 36, col. 4—who survives, plans to assume a larger role in management of the universe.)

Reaction from the world's great and from the man in the street was uniformly incredulous. "At least he's out of his misery," commented one housewife in an Elmira, N.Y., supermarket. "I can't believe it," said the Right Reverend Horace W. B. Donegan, Protestant Episcopal Bishop of New York, who only last week celebrated the 15th anniversary of his installation as Bishop. In Paris, President de Gaulle, in a 30 second appearance on national television, proclaimed: "God is dead! Long live the republic! Long live France!" Mrs. Jacqueline Kennedy, widow of the late President, was reported "in seclusion" in her Fifth Avenue apartment. "She's had about all she can take," a close friend of the Kennedy family said. News of the death was included in a one-sentence statement, without comment, on the 3rd page of Pravda, official organ of the Soviet Government. The passing of God has not been disclosed to the 800 million Chinese who live behind the bamboo curtain.

Public reaction in this country was perhaps summed up by an elderly retired streetcar conductor in Passaic, New Jersey, who said: "I never met him, of course. Never even saw him. But from what I heard I guess he was a real nice fellow. Tops." From Independence, Mo., former President Harry S Truman, who received the news in his Kansas City barbershop, said: "I'm always sorry to hear somebody is dead. It's a damn shame." In Gettysburg, Pa., former President Dwight D. Eisenhower, released, through a military aide, the following statement: "Mrs. Eisenhower joins me in heartfelt sympathy to the family and many friends of the late God. He was, I always felt, a force for moral good in the universe. Those of us who were privileged to know him admired the probity of his character, the breadth of his compassion, the depth of his intellect. Generous almost to a fault, his many acts of kindness to America will never be forgotten. It is a very great loss indeed. He will be missed."

From Basel, Switzerland, came word that Dr. Karl Barth, venerable Protestant theologian, informed of the death of God, declared: "I don't know who died in Atlanta, but whoever he was he's an imposter." Dr. Barth, 79, with the late Paul Tillich, is widely regarded as the foremost theologian of the Twentieth Century.

(There have been unconfirmed reports that Jesus of Nazareth, 33, a carpenter and reputed son of God, who survives, will assume the authority, if not the title, of the deceased deity. Jesus, sometimes called the Christ, was himself a victim of death, having succumbed some 1932 years ago in Palestine, now the state of Israel, purportedly on orders of a Roman governor, Pontius Pilate, and at the behest of certain citizens of Jerusalem. This event, described by some as "deicide," has lately occupied the deliberations of the Vatican Council, which has solemnly exonerated the Jews generally of responsibility for the alleged crime. The case is complicated by the fact that Jesus, although he died, returned to life, and so may not have died at all. Diplomats around the world were speculating today on the place the resurrected Jesus will occupy in the power vacuum created by the sudden passing of God.)

Dr. Altizer, God's surgeon, in an exclusive interview with the Times, stated this morning that the death was "not unexpected." "He had been ailing for some time," Dr. Altizer said, "and lived much longer than most of us thought possible." He noted that the death of God had, in fact, been prematurely announced in the last century by the famed German surgeon, Nietzsche. Nietzsche, who was insane the last ten years of his life, may have confused "certain symptoms of morbidity in the aged patient with actual death, a mistake any busy surgeon will occasionally make," Dr. Altizer suggested. "God was an excellent patient, compliant, cheerful, alert. Every comfort modern science could provide was made available to him. He did not suffer— he just, as it were, slipped out of our grasp." Dr. Alitzer also disclosed that plans for a memorial to God have already been discussed informally, and it is likely a committee of eminent clergymen and laymen will soon be named to raise funds for use in "research into the causes of death in deities, an area of medicine many physicians consider has been too long neglected." Dr. Altizer indicated, finally, that he had great personal confidence that Jesus, relieved of the burdens of divinity, would, in time, assume a position of great importance in the universe. "We have lost," he said, "a father, but we have gained a son."

(Next Sunday's *New York Times* will include, without extra charge, a 24-page full-color supplement with many photographs, reviewing the major events of God's long reign, the circumstances of his sudden and untimely death, and prospects for a godless future. The editors will be grateful for pertinent letters, photographs, visions and the like.)

There has been as yet no statement from Jesus, but a close associate, the Holy Ghost, has urged prayer and good works. He also said that it is the wish of the family that in lieu of flowers contributions be made to the Building Fund for the Cathedral of St. John the Divine in New York City so that the edifice may be finished.